Zen

MASTER CLASS

JOURNAL

A GODSFIELD BOOK

First published in Great Britain in 2002 by Godsfield Press Ltd
Laurel House, Station Approach, Alresford, Hampshire SO24 9JH, U.K.

2 4 6 8 10 9 7 5 3 1

Designed for Godsfield Press by
The Bridgewater Book Company

Printed and bound in China

ISBN 1–84181–157–2

*Worldly fools search for exotic masters, not
realizing that their own mind is the master.*

BODHIDHARMA

When studying Zen and seeking Buddhahood,
don't see Buddhahood as the goal.
If you do, it will become further away.

DOGEN

Find the silence which contains thoughts.

H A K U I N

I haven't got any Buddhism.
I live by letting things happen.

DOGEN

*You have two eyes, to see both the relative and
the absolute.
Don't see through one only, for then you will
be partially sighted.*

BAIZHANG

Zen MASTER CLASS

*Our Buddha-nature is there from the very
beginning.
It is like the sun emerging from behind clouds.
It is like a mirror that reflects perfectly when it is
wiped clean and returned to its original clarity.*

HO-SHAN

Zen MASTER CLASS

The limitless sky of meditation.
The clear moonlight of wisdom.
The truth revealed as eternal stillness.
This earth is the pure lotus-land.
This body is the body of the Buddha.

HAKUIN

*When the sudden doctrine is understood there is
no need to discipline yourself in external things.
If you always have the right view within your
mind, you will never be deluded.
This is seeing into your own nature.*

HUINENG, PLATFORM SUTRA

If you wish to find the Buddha, first you must look into your own mind; outside of the mind, there is no Buddha.

HAKUIN

What is it, the heart?
It is the sound of the pine breeze in the black ink
painting.

IKKYU

Zen MASTER CLASS

An ancient pond
A frog jumps in
The sound of water

BASHO

What shall be my legacy?
The blossoms of the spring,
The cuckoo in the hills,
The leaves of the autumn.

RYOKAN

I have not heard of a single Buddha,
past or present, who has been enlightened
by sacred prayers and scriptures.

BASSUI

When you try to stop doing to achieve being,
this very effort fills you with doing.

SENGCAN

Zen MASTER CLASS

Zen MASTER CLASS

> *Outwardly in the world of good and evil,*
> *yet without thoughts stirring the heart—*
> *this is meditation.*
> *Inwardly seeing one's own true nature and not*
> *being distracted from it—this is meditation.*

HUINENG

Zen MASTER CLASS

You can't prevent time passing.
When something has passed,
why do thoughts still loiter?

RYOKAN

A day without work is a day without food.

BAIZHANG

A special transmission outside the scriptures;
No dependence upon words and letters;
Direct pointing at the mind;
Seeing into one's nature and the attainment
of buddhahood.

BODHIDHARMA

The way is unconnected with knowing and not knowing. Knowing is to have a concept, while not knowing is to be ignorant. If you realize the way that is beyond doubt, it is like the sky— vast open emptiness.

ZHAOZHOU

When I'm through with thinking
I wander in the woods
gathering handfuls of flowers.

RYOKAN

All the profound doctrines are but a speck of dust in a vast void.
All the great affairs of the world are but a drop of water cast into a bottomless chasm.

DESHAN

*If you use your mind to try and understand
reality, you will understand neither your mind
nor reality.
If your try and understand reality without using
your mind, you will understand both your mind
and reality.*

BODHIDHARMA

On leaf and grass
Awaiting the morning sun,
The dew quickly evaporates away.

DOGEN

Of all things, the mind is fundamental; all phenomena are simply products of the mind. Therefore know that all good and evil arises from your own mind. To seek Enlightenment somewhere outside of the mind is an utter impossibility.

SHENXIU

If you wish to understand the path, the ordinary mind is the path. What is called the ordinary mind? It is to be without deliberate actions, without distinguishing right and wrong, grasping and rejecting, or ordinary and holy.

MAZU

MASTER CLASS

*When there is nothing more within you, do
not engage in useless seeking. What is found by
useless seeking is no gain. When your mind is
without anything and you are no-mind, then you
are free and spiritual, empty and marvelous.*

DESHAN

When hunger comes, I eat my rice;
When sleep comes, I close my eyes.
Fools laugh at me,
but the wise understand.

LINJI

*The very impermanency of grass and trees ...
of people and things, body and mind, is the
Buddha-nature.*

DOGEN

Zen MASTER CLASS

Recollection of the Buddha aims to liberate one from the cycle of birth and death; Zen practice seeks to realize one's primordial nature.

JAKUSHITSU

The real Buddha, which is nothing other than the essence of all things, the master of seeing, hearing, and perceiving.

BASSUI

The winter seagull—
No home in life,
No grave in death.

RYOKON